RESCUE

Written by **Bridget Joyce**

Illustrated by **The Illusion Academy ArtWorks**

You will know it is time to turn the page when you hear this sound.... Now listen along as Tonka rescue trucks move into their new firehouse and battle a fire at an abandoned paint factory.

publications international, ltd.

1

The city's fireboat leaves the dock and glides through the bay on a sunny day. The fireboat operator and firefighters enjoy the ride to their new fire station. Once there, the fireboat, other rescue vehicles, and brave firefighters will work together to protect the city from dangerous fires.

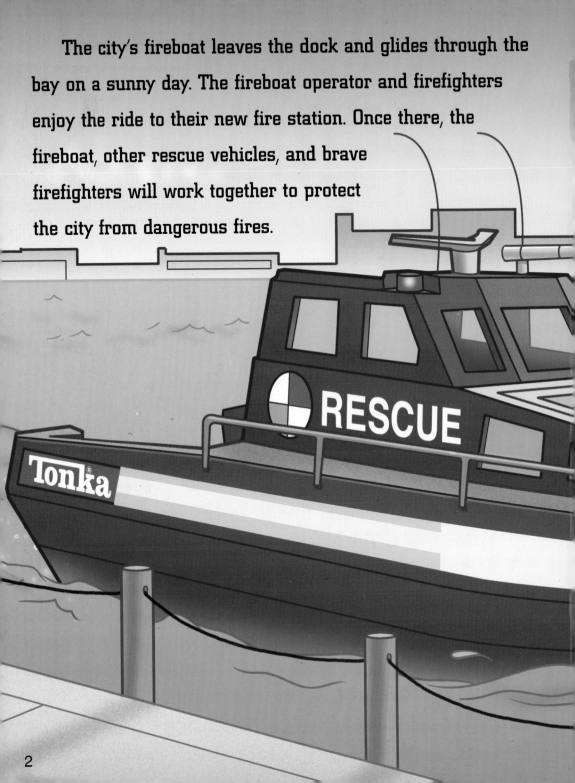

The boat pulls up to the fire station. The crew
docks the boat and walks to the front of the building.

4

In front of the fire station, a compactor rolls back and forth over the asphalt driveway. Huge drums under the compactor shake as they smooth and flatten the hot, black asphalt.

The compactor stops. Now the building and its driveway are finished. Tomorrow more rescue vehicles will move into their new home.

The next morning, two fire engines cross the driveway and park inside the fire station. These trucks carry water, a hose, firefighters, and other tools used to fight fires. Firefighters inspect the 500-gallon water tanks on each engine. They check the trucks' compartments to make sure all of the tools they may need are there.

Soon an aerial truck
arrives with big ladders and
platforms along with smaller ground ladders and
important tools. Firefighters need ladders. They climb
ladders to rescue people from burning buildings. They
stand on ladder platforms to spray water at fire from above.
Sometimes they use ladders to get on top of a building to
break holes in its roof.

An ambulance takes its place in the new fire station. Fires are dangerous, and people sometimes get hurt. Many firefighters know emergency first aid. They bring the ambulance to fires in case someone needs help.

Firefighters keep medical equipment inside the ambulance so they can help people as soon as they reach them. The ambulance also has flashing lights and sirens so it can drive quickly to the hospital. Sometimes the firehouse ambulance responds to medical emergencies that have nothing to do with a fire.

A special truck with a laboratory inside of it pulls into the garage. Firefighters use this truck when they go to fires where chemicals may burn. Inside the truck, they can test air, water, and soil samples from the site of the fire to find out if the area is safe for people. If a chemical escapes the fire, the firefighters make sure no people get hurt.

Finally the communications and command van parks in the garage. From this van, the fire chief directs the firefighters and talks to the command center. The chief keeps radios and maps inside the van. When he needs help, he can radio the command center to send more trucks.

FIRE DEPT.
DIAL 9-1-1

Tonk

Suddenly a plume of thick, black smoke begins to rise over the bay. The fire alarm rings!

The aerial truck races out of the garage first, followed by the two fire engines. An abandoned paint factory on the bay is on fire. One by one, the other vehicles leave the garage and head toward the factory.

The emergency vehicles speed through the city streets, sirens wailing and lights flashing. Cars and other vehicles pull aside to let these big, loud trucks pass. Three firefighters hurry into the fireboat and speed away to the fire.

At the fire, the chief takes charge in his command van. Some firefighters raise the ladders while others hook hoses into the fire engine and connect them to the fire truck.

The aerial truck lifts a firefighter into the air. He attacks the flames with a powerful jet of water from above. While the firefighter sprays water on the flames, nozzles on the cage at the top of the ladder spray him with water. The water keeps him cool while he battles the fire.

Meanwhile rescue workers gather air, soil, and water. They take the samples to the laboratory truck. The rescue workers perform tests to see if the air, water, and soil are clean. Fortunately no chemicals have escaped the paint factory. This truck has done its job and returns to the fire station.

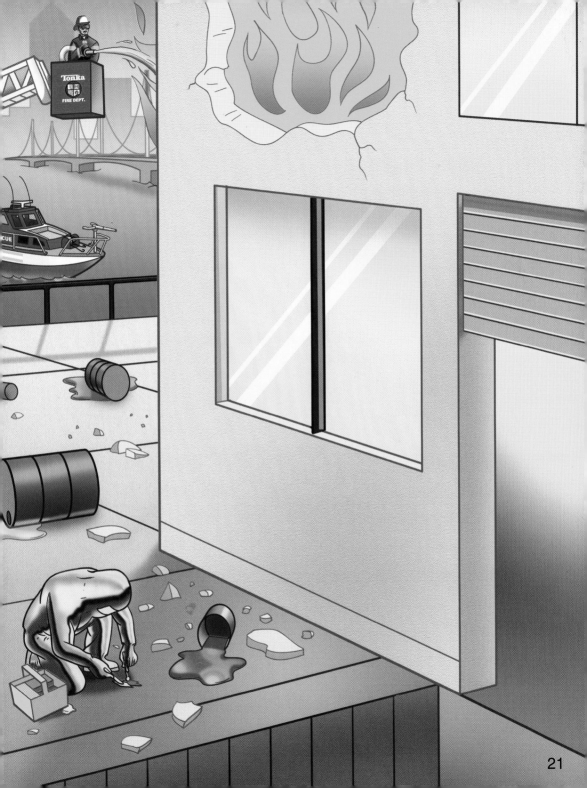

On the other side of the factory, firefighters on the
fireboat blast streams of water at the burning building.
Pumps underneath the bright red boat suck in water from
the bay and shoot it 300 feet in the air through powerful
water cannons. These firefighters never worry about running
out of water because the boat takes water from the bay.